The World is full of BABIES!

Mick Manning and Brita Granström

W
FRANKLIN WATTS
LONDON•SYDNEY

Not all eggs are laid in nests.
You were an egg once. Then you
developed inside your mum like this.

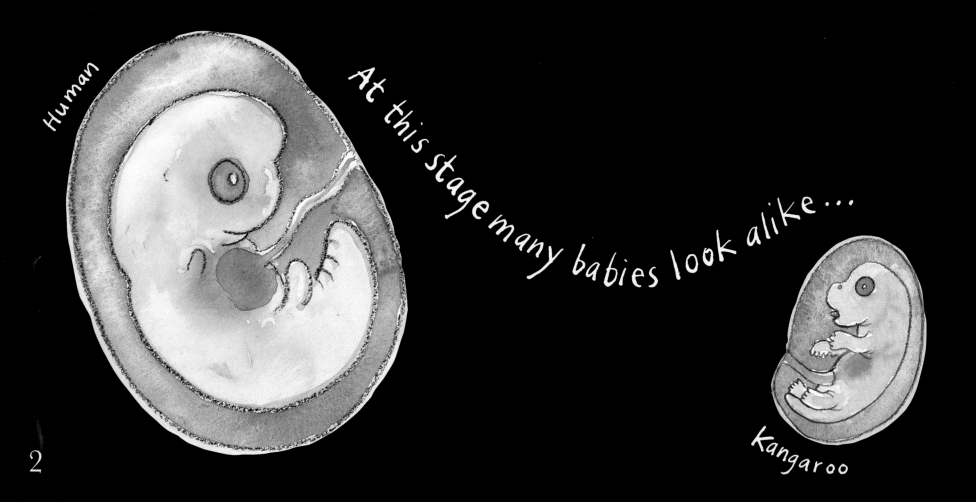

Human

At this stage many babies look alike...

Kangaroo

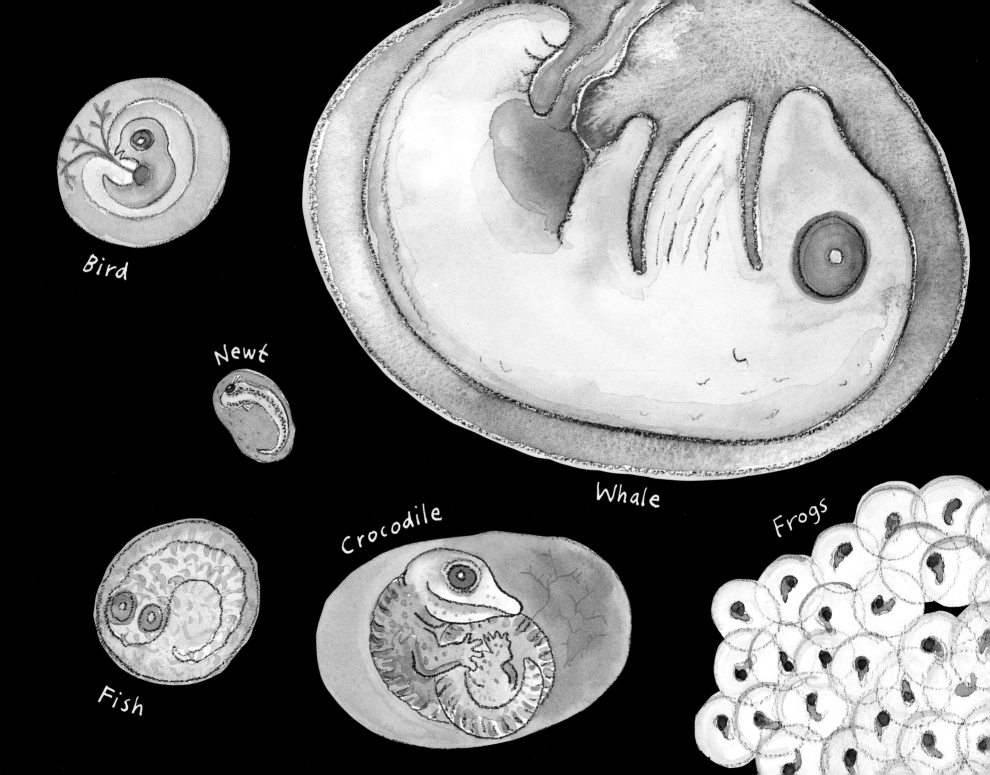

Bird

Newt

Whale

Crocodile

Frogs

Fish

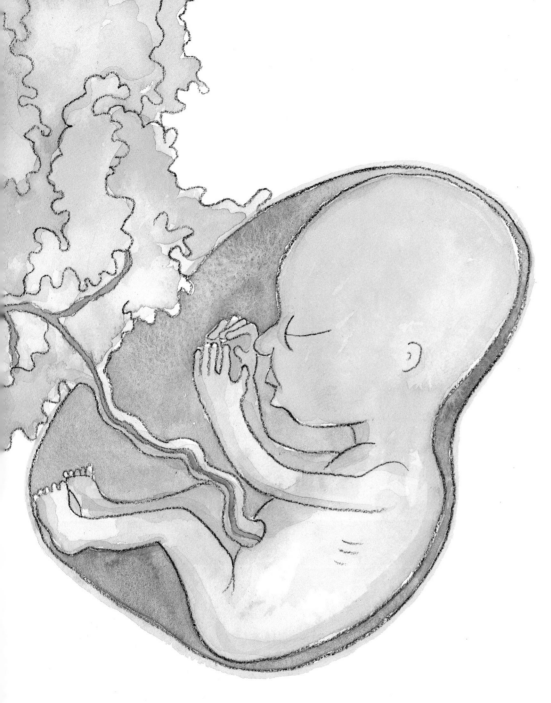

All over the earth, babies are growing.

It took nine months for you to grow big enough to be born.

It takes nine weeks for a puppy to grow and be born...

It takes two years for an elephant to grow and be born...

It takes twenty one days for a house mouse...

All over the earth, babies are being born.

You were born in a warm room.

If you had a cuckoo for a mum, the first thing you would do after you hatched is push all the other eggs out of the nest...

If you had a polar bear for a mum you'd be born in a snow den in the middle of winter...

Maaaaa

All over the earth, babies are crying.

You often used to cry for your mum.

Aaaaahhh!!

Parents and babies quickly learn the sound of each other's voices...

Rhino calves **SQUEAL!**

Chicks... Cheep Cheep...

Hamsters... **SQUEAK!**

Puppies whimper

All over the earth, babies are suckling.
You suckled your mum's milk.

Some babies drink milk from a bottle ...

10

Piglets and tiger cubs, monkeys and humans... – all baby mammals drink **MILK!**

If you were a sealpup you'd drink such rich, fatty milk that you would be three times fatter in just a few days...

11

All over the earth, babies are sleeping.
You slept cosy in a cot with blankets and
gentle music.

If you were a bat baby
you'd sleep upside down,
hanging on with tiny
fingernails in a draughty
old roof space...

If you were a sea bird chick you'd sleep through a storm perched on a cliff high above the sea...

If you were a whale baby you'd float alongside mum with all the sea for a bed and whale song for a lullaby...

13

All over the earth, babies are being carried around. Perhaps you were carried around outdoors in a sort of baby rucksack.

If you were a lemur baby you'd have to cling on tight!

If you were a kangaroo baby you'd sit comfy in a pouch and peep out...

If you were a crocodile baby you'd ride between mum's big TEETH!

All over the earth, babies are growing up.
It took about six months before you
began to crawl across the rug.

But think about this........if you were a baby rat you would be an adult in three months with a family of your own and you could have twenty babies every six weeks.

That means three months later you'd be a grandparent with four hundred grandchildren.
And three months after that you'd have... **8,000** great grandchildren!

All over the earth, babies are getting dirty!
You couldn't keep yourself clean when you were a baby,
so you wore a nappy and had to be bathed every day.

If you were a kingfisher baby you'd sit happily in a stinking mess of rotten fishbones and droppings!

If you were a cat or a polecat kitten you would be licked clean every day by your mum's rough tongue...

All over the earth, babies are learning to walk. You began to walk at about twelve months.

Many predators are waiting to eat baby animals...

If you were a fawn you'd have to be able to jump and run within an hour of being born...

If you were a new butterfly you could take to the air as soon as your wings dried in the sun...

If you were a tiny turtle you'd hurry to the sea as soon as you hatched...

If you were a baby adder you'd be very poisonous ...

All over the earth, babies are learning their own language. You started to talk at about two years old. First you said "mum" or "dad", then other words came out and you slowly learned to join them together.

If you were a lion cub you'd be learning how to roar...

If you were a honey bee you'd do the "sundance" to show where the best pollen can be found...

If you were an otter you'd learn to whistle...

If you were a wolf cub you'd be learning the howls and calls of your pack...

All over the earth, babies are exploring –
holding hands to stay safe.
Perhaps you still hold mum's hand.

But if you were one of a shrew family you would hold tails...

All over the earth, babies are playing.
You played hide and seek and tag.

Lots of animals play chasing and hiding games – it's practice for hunting or escaping...

All over the earth, babies are becoming
adults who can have babies of their own.
One day, maybe you will have a baby too.

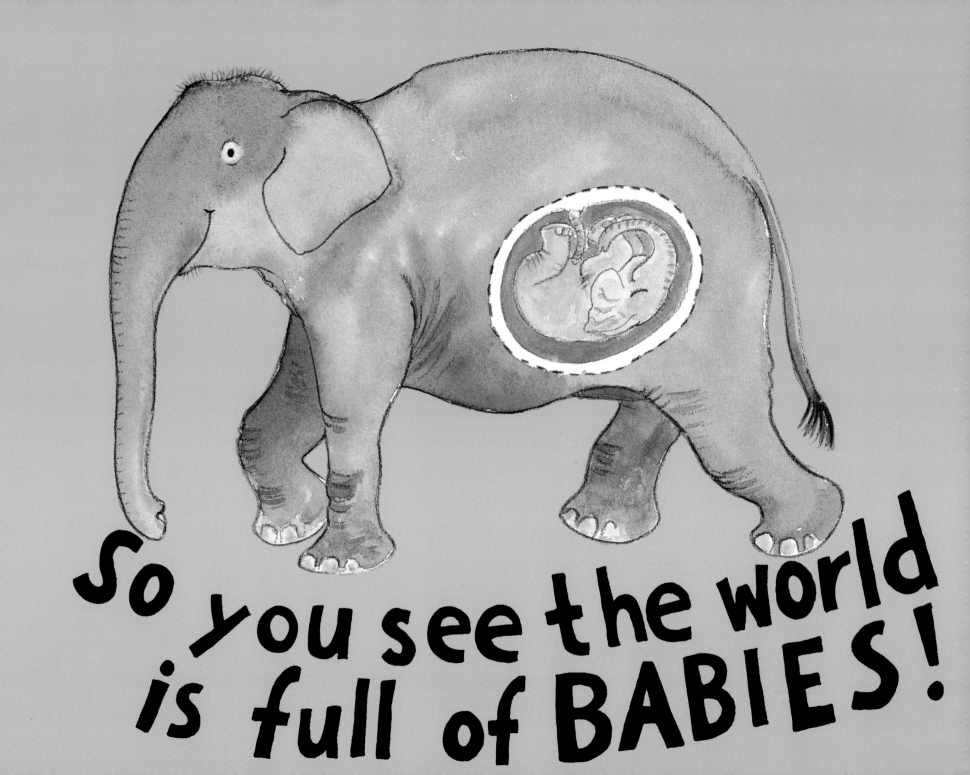

So you see the world is full of BABIES!

Useful words

Cuckoo (page 7) a cuckoo lays its eggs in another bird's nest. Animals that pick on another animal to rear their babies are called parasites.

Egg (page 2) an egg is the beginning of a baby. Some animals lay their eggs, but other animals and most mammals make eggs that develop inside their body and are born as babies.

Mammals (page 11) mammals are warm-blooded animals that feed their young on milk. Humans are mammals – so are whales, monkeys and thousands of other animals.

Pollen (page 23) a special dust in plants that bees use to feed their young.

Pouch (page 15) a sort of skin bag under the belly of animals like kangaroos. It is for carrying a baby.

Predator (page 21) an animal that hunts and eats other animals.

Snow den (page 7) a female polar bear digs a home under the snow to have her cubs – we call it a den.

Suckle (page 10) the way baby mammals drink their milk.

Whale song (page 13) whales sing to each other – their songs can travel thousands of miles across the ocean.

To our parents, with love – MM & BG

This edition 2014

First published by Franklin Watts, 338 Euston Road, London NW1 3BH

Franklin Watts Australia, Level 17 / 207 Kent Street, Sydney NSW 2000

Text and illustrations © 1996 Mick Manning and Brita Granström
Notes and activities © 2004, 2014 Franklin Watts

The illustrations in this book were made by Brita and Mick.
Find out more about Mick and Brita at www.mickandbrita.com

Series editor: Paula Borton

A CIP catalogue record is available from the British Library.
Dewey Classification 305.23

Printed in China

ISBN 978 1 4451 2894 8

Franklin Watts is a division of Hachette Children's Books,
an Hachette UK company. www.hachette.co.uk